El cerdo

Lee Waters

A este cerdo le gusta
el agua.

A este cerdo le gusta
el lodo.

A este cerdo le gusta
el pasto.

A estos cerdos les gusta oler.

A estos cerdos les gusta
escarbar.

A estos cerdos les gusta jugar.

orejas

hocico

rabo

patas

Houseboat on the Everglades

by Michael Sandler
illustrated by Nancy Lane

SCHOOL PUBLISHERS

Copyright © by Harcourt, Inc.

All rights reserved. No part of this publication may be reproduced or transmitted in any form or by any means, electronic or mechanical, including photocopy, recording, or any information storage and retrieval system, without permission in writing from the publisher.

Requests for permission to make copies of any part of the work should be addressed to School Permissions and Copyrights, Harcourt, Inc., 6277 Sea Harbor Drive, Orlando, Florida 32887–6777. Fax: 407-345-2418.

HARCOURT and the Harcourt Logo are trademarks of Harcourt, Inc., registered in the United States of America and/or other jurisdictions.

Printed in Mexico

ISBN 10: 0-15-350281-9
ISBN 13: 978-0-15-350281-1

Ordering Options
ISBN 10: 0-15-349940-0 (Grade 5 ELL Collection)
ISBN 13: 978-0-15-349940-1 (Grade 5 ELL Collection)
ISBN 10: 0-15-357317-1 (package of 5)
ISBN 13: 978-0-15-357317-0 (package of 5)

2 3 4 5 6 7 8 9 10   126   12 11 10 09 08 07

"Four days in a swamp?" I said.

"Four days on a boat?" my brother, Tommy, said.

"You must be joking!" Tommy and I said at the same time.

"I am not," said our mom.

We looked at her face. She was serious. She wasn't joking. Tommy and I had been looking forward to this vacation for weeks. We had big plans. Unfortunately, we hadn't told Mom about them yet.

We wanted to play baseball. Both of us wanted to be on the summer league team. Being chosen for the team wasn't going to be easy. We couldn't afford to miss any practice. We really needed it.

Now we were going to the Everglades in Florida to spend four days on a boat. We were going to miss too much practice to be ready for tryouts. Our plans to play baseball would have to wait until next summer.

I knew a little bit about the Everglades. We had studied the Everglades in science class. The Everglades is a big swamp. A swamp is an area of land that always has some shallow water covering it. Walking around a swamp isn't easy.

The best way to explore the Everglades is by boat. That's why we were renting a houseboat. A houseboat is like a floating apartment. We would float during the day. We would stop and sleep at night.

Tommy wasn't happy about the boat part. He took a ferry once. The water was rough. He was seasick in five minutes. Mom said this was different. The water wasn't rough. Tommy didn't believe her.

I wasn't happy about the swamp part. Swamps are full of animals like alligators and snakes. Bugs are everywhere. A lot of mosquitoes live in swamps! I didn't like insects that bite. Tommy and I didn't want to go. Still, we had no choice. Mom would not change her mind.

My mom, Tommy, and I had arrived at the Everglades. The three of us were standing on a dock. Tommy and I looked down between the wooden boards. We stared into the water. Were there alligators down there? I couldn't see any. I could see mosquitoes. They buzzed around my face. I was bitten twice in just a few minutes. We looked at the houseboat. This would be our home for four days. Jack, the boat's owner, was waiting for us.

"Hello, Captain," Jack said to my mom. He helped her step into the boat. He pointed to Tommy and me. "You two must be the crew. Every captain needs a good crew to do work. Come aboard."

Tommy and I stepped onto the boat. Jack showed us around. I had never been on a boat before, unlike Tommy. I thought the boat was nice. Jack showed us around the boat. He started with the front and back of the boat. The front was the bow. The back was the stern. The name of our boat, *Esmeralda*, was painted on the stern.

"Where are the sails?" I asked.

"We have no sails," laughed Jack. "This isn't a sailboat. This boat is not powered by wind. A gas engine keeps this boat moving."

I felt silly. Still, what did I know about boats? Jack showed us the cabin. It was like a little house on top of the boat. We would sleep and eat there. Each side of the cabin had windows. Jack told us to keep them closed. If we didn't, we would have mosquitoes. He didn't have to tell me twice.

Chairs, a table, a kitchen, and sleeping bunks were inside. The cabin was just like an apartment.

The lower deck was outside. The lower deck was around the cabin. You could walk on the deck all the way around the boat. The upper deck was on the roof of the cabin. You had clear views from there. Nothing stood in your way.

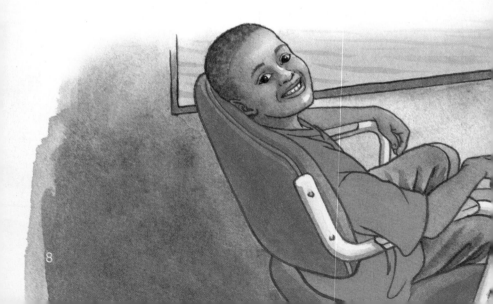

Jack showed my mom how everything worked on the boat. He showed her how to change the ship's direction. He raised and lowered the anchor.

"The anchor holds a boat in place," said Jack. "Use it at night. The boat will drift, or float away, if you don't. You could end up way out in the ocean."

Jack also showed us the gas tank. "No flames around here," he said. "No candles or matches. Gas is very dangerous and can cause big fires."

I was getting excited. Tommy still looked worried. "What if I get seasick?" he said.

"You won't," said Jack. "The water is very calm. It's time for you to put the cargo on the boat." He pointed to our bags sitting on the dock. "Then you can start your trip."

"Remember to listen to your captain," Jack said. "A captain is in charge of a ship." This wasn't a new job for mom. She was captain at home, too.

The *Esmeralda* was moving now. Jack waved good-bye. Tommy and I were surprised. The ride was smooth! Our captain was skilled. Mom looked calm at the wheel of the boat.

The boat glided through the water. The grassy marsh was on either side of us. Birds were everywhere. They hopped in and out of the water, looking for fish.

We traveled through the Everglades over the next four days. We passed from open water to narrow strips of water. We entered into open water again. The trip was never dull. There was always something to see.

Fish popped out of the water. We saw a dolphin once. We saw alligators, too. The alligators' long faces and huge teeth were frightening. We were safe, though. The alligators could not get onto our boat.

We dropped anchor every afternoon. That meant it was time to stop for the day. Making dinner was a job for me and Tommy.

"Get to work, crew," my mom would say to us.

Tommy and I did our best. We didn't make anything fancy, just grilled sandwiches or spaghetti. The meals always tasted great, though. Boating made you hungry. Food tasted better after a day on the water.

Sleeping was also better on a boat. The Everglades were much quieter than where we lived. Water hitting the boat and the hum of insects were the only sounds we heard.

The only things that weren't great were the mosquitoes. The worst times were early morning and early evening. The air was thick with bugs during those times. Even bug spray didn't keep them away. You couldn't fight them. You had to hide. We stayed inside the cabin during those times.

After four days, we returned to the dock where we had started. Jack was there to meet us.

"How did it go?" he asked.

"I love the Everglades," I said.

"I love boats," Tommy said.

"I am sure you'll be seeing us again soon," said Mom.

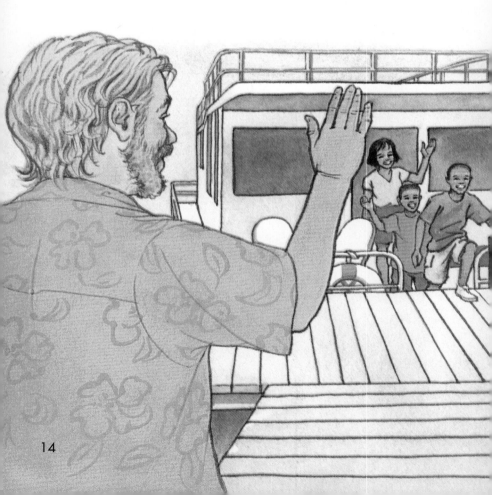

Scaffolded Language Development

PRONOUN *You* Have students look back at each of the following sentences from the book.

> *You could walk on the deck all the way around the boat.* (page 8)
> *Boating made you hungry.* (page 12)
> *You couldn't fight them. You had to hide.* (page 13)

Ask students who the pronoun *you* refers to in each sentence. If necessary, reread the page with the sentence to help establish context. Point out to students that the pronoun *you* in these sentences doesn't take the place of any particular person. Each sentence is a general statement about anybody who might be on a boat.

Have students pretend they are the teacher, and ask them to say aloud general sentences using the word *you*. If necessary, help them get started with several examples: *You should take notes during class. You should bring your books home to study.*

 Social Studies

Famous Boats Have students find facts about famous boats in the history of the United States. Tell them to choose one boat, and create a fact sheet detailing its history and fate.

School-Home Connection

Family Trip Have students ask a friend or family member whether they have ever taken a vacation or a trip to a new place. If so, have them ask what they liked or disliked about their trip.

Word Count: 1,154